Virginia
Standards of
Learning *Success*

POWERED BY
GO Math!

INCLUDES

- Virginia Standards of Learning Lessons
- Lesson Practice/Homework with Spiral Review

Table of Contents

Name _____

Ordinal Numbers

Essential Question How are ordinal numbers used?

Learning Objective You will use ordinal numbers to identify position or order.

Listen and Draw (Real World)

Look at the sentence below.
The letter W is the first letter in the sentence.

We use math every day.

Math Talk Math Processes and Practices **7**

Explain how to find the tenth letter in the sentence.

 FOR THE TEACHER • Read the following problem. • Draw a line under the second letter in the sentence. Circle the sixth letter in the sentence.

Model and Draw

Ordinal numbers are used to tell about position or order.

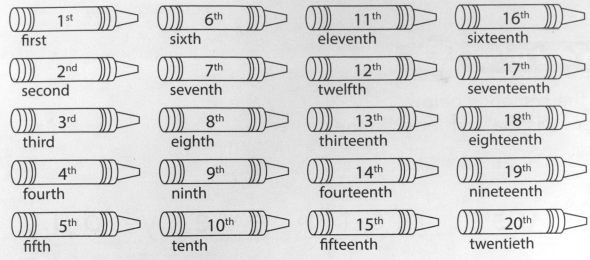

1st first	6th sixth	11th eleventh	16th sixteenth
2nd second	7th seventh	12th twelfth	17th seventeenth
3rd third	8th eighth	13th thirteenth	18th eighteenth
4th fourth	9th ninth	14th fourteenth	19th nineteenth
5th fifth	10th tenth	15th fifteenth	20th twentieth

Color the twelfth crayon red. Color the 17th crayon blue.

Share and Show

Circle and mark an X to show position.

first

1. Circle the sixth bag.

2. Mark an X on the 11th bag.

3. In what position is the 🛍 ? _____

4. How many bags are in front of the twentieth bag?

_____

On Your Own

Write an ordinal number to answer each question.

5. What position is just before 6th? _____

6. What position is just after 18th? _____

7. Write the missing ordinal numbers.

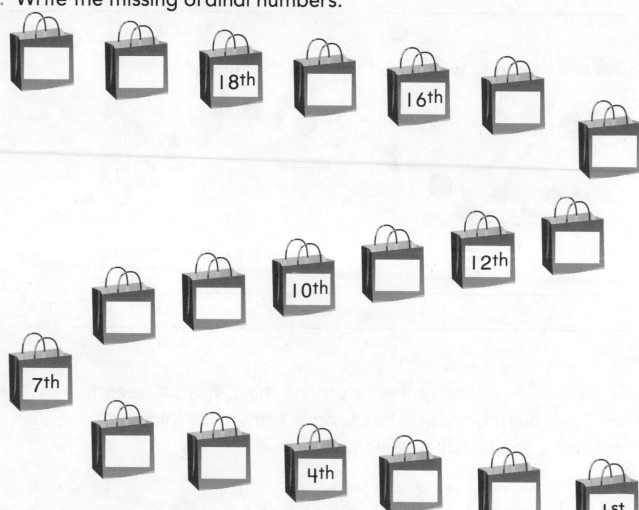

8. **GO DEEPER** Karen draws 20 circles. She colors the first circle red, the second circle blue, and the third circle green. If she continues coloring in that pattern, what color will the twentieth circle be? Draw a picture to help you.

_____

Problem Solving • Applications  WRITE Math

9. The second grade classes are visiting the science center. Mark is fourteenth in line to see the space exhibit. How many children are in line in front of him?

10. The children are waiting in line to see the dinosaur exhibit at the science center. Delia is ninth in line. Caleb is thirteenth in line. How many children are between them?

11. GO DEEPER Randy was asked to circle the tenth fruit.

first

Describe his mistake. Which fruit should he have circled?

_____

_____

12. THINK SMARTER Jill has a bracelet. The third, fifth, sixteenth, and twentieth beads on her bracelet are red. Color to show the red beads on Jill's bracelet.

first

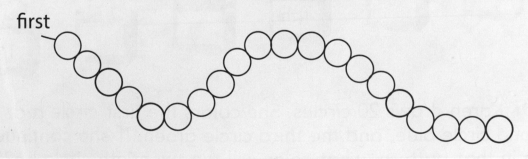

 TAKE HOME ACTIVITY • Ask your child how he or she solved one of the problems on this page.

Ordinal Numbers

Circle and mark an X to show position.

Learning Objective You will use ordinal numbers to identify position or order.

first

1. Circle the fifteenth fish.

2. Draw an X on the 7th fish.

3. Which fish has stripes? Write your answer.

The _____ fish has stripes.

Problem Solving

4. There are 20 dogs in a line.

   Ruff is twelfth in line. Winnie is fourteenth in line.

   Opie is between them.

   Write the ordinal number to tell where Opie is. _____

5. **WRITE** **Math** Neo and Brad are standing in line. Neo is 20th in line. Brad is five places in front of Neo. What is Brad's position in line? How can you find the answer?

_____

_____

_____

Lesson Check

1. Which pencil is fourteenth in the row? Circle your answer.

first

Spiral Review

2. Tina is the nineteenth person in line. How many people are in front of her?

   ○ 8
   ○ 8
   ○ 18
   ○ 20

3. Which number comes next?

   26, 27, 28, 29, ___

   ○ 28
   ○ 30
   ○ 38
   ○ 40

4. Circle and mark an X to show position.

first

Circle the 17th star.
Mark an X on the third star.
Draw a line under the 7th star.

Model and Draw

Find the part that repeats. Use this **pattern core** to extend the pattern.

Draw shapes to extend the pattern.

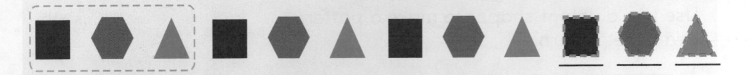

Write numbers to extend the pattern.

2 4 6   2 4 6   2____ 4____ 6____

Share and Show

Circle the pattern core. Then draw shapes or write numbers to extend the pattern.

✓ 1.

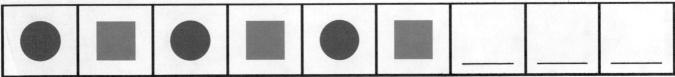

2.

3. 10 20 10 20 10 20 ____ ____ ____

✓ 4. 8 9 10 8 9 10 8 9 10 ____ ____ ____

Name _____

Algebra • Repeating Patterns

Essential Question How can you extend a repeating pattern?

Learning Objective You will identify, describe, and extend repeating patterns.

Listen and Draw

Use two different shapes to make a pattern. Draw the pattern.

Math Talk

How can you tell if a row of shapes makes a pattern?

HOME CONNECTION • Your child made a pattern using shapes. This activity prepares children for working with patterns in the next few lessons.

Problem Solving • Applications  WRITE Math

11. **GO DEEPER** Use circles of different colors to make a pattern. Draw the first 12 circles in your pattern.

Tell about the pattern core you used.

_____

_____

_____

12. **THINK SMARTER** Cathy is using a pattern to make a necklace with beads.

Which bead will Cathy use next?

○ ☐

○ ●

○ ☐

○ ○

 TAKE HOME ACTIVITY • Make a repeating pattern with objects. Have your child describe the pattern core and tell what comes next in the pattern.

Name _____

On Your Own

Circle the pattern core. Then draw shapes or write numbers to extend the pattern.

5.

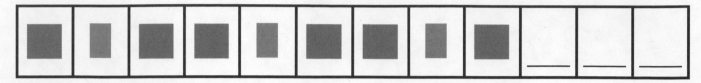

6.

7. Go DEEPER

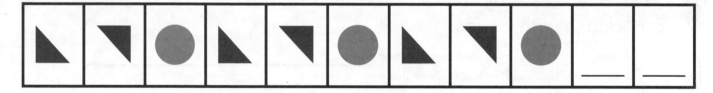

8. 6 7 8 6 7 8 6 7 8 ___ ___ ___

9. 15 16 15 16 15 16 ___ ___ ___

10. 4 8 12 16 4 8 12 16 ___ ___ ___

Lesson Check

1. Circle the pattern core. Then draw a shape to extend the pattern.

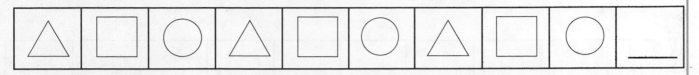

Spiral Review

2. Which number is greater than 25?

   ○ 15
   ○ 20
   ○ 23
   ○ 28

3. Which number is less than 68?

   ○ 44
   ○ 69
   ○ 75
   ○ 90

4. Use tens and ones to describe the number 92.

   _____ tens _____ ones

5. What number can be written as 7 tens and 4 ones? Write the number.

   _____

Algebra • Repeating Patterns

Learning Objective You will identify, describe, and extend repeating patterns.

Circle the pattern core. Then draw shapes or write numbers to extend the pattern.

1.
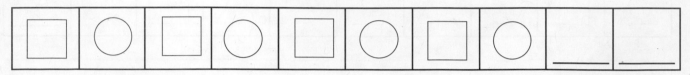

2.
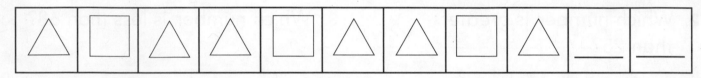

3.
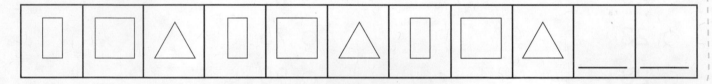

4. 3 4 5 3 4 5 3 4 5 ___ ___ ___

5. 9 10 9 10 9 10 ___ ___ ___ ___

Problem Solving Real World

6. Eileen is using a pattern to make a beaded necklace. Draw the next bead she will put on her necklace.

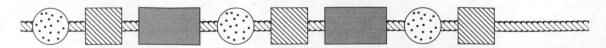

Name _____

Algebra • Repeating Patterns

Essential Question How can you extend a repeating pattern?

Learning Objective You will identify, describe, and extend repeating patterns.

Listen and Draw

Use two different shapes to make a pattern.
Draw the pattern.

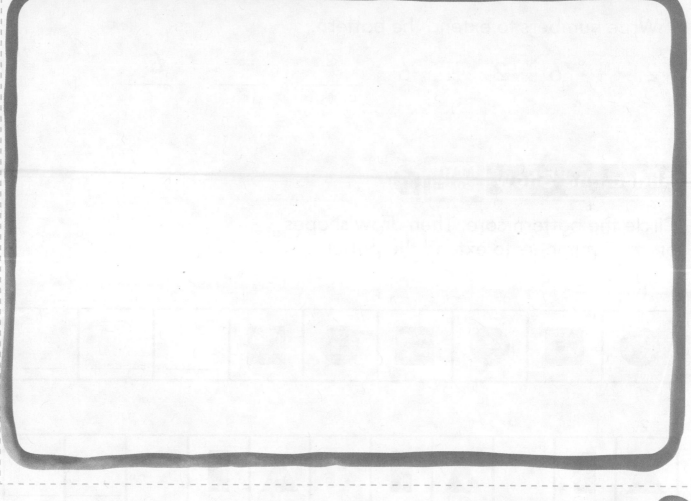

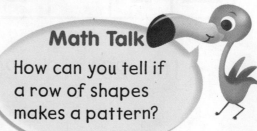

Math Talk

How can you tell if a row of shapes makes a pattern?

HOME CONNECTION • Your child made a pattern using shapes. This activity prepares children for working with patterns in the next few lessons.

Model and Draw

Find the part that repeats. Use this **pattern core** to extend the pattern.

Draw shapes to extend the pattern.

Write numbers to extend the pattern.

2 4 6 2 4 6 _2_ _4_ _6_

Share and Show MATH BOARD

Circle the pattern core. Then draw shapes or write numbers to extend the pattern.

✓ 1.

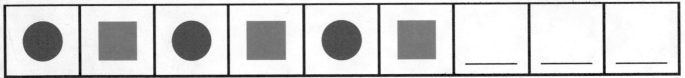

2.

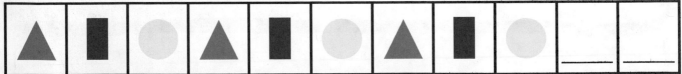

3. 10 20 10 20 10 20 _____ _____

✓ 4. 8 9 10 8 9 10 8 9 10 _____ _____

Name _____

Algebra • Growing Patterns

Essential Question How can you extend a growing pattern?

Learning Objective You will identify, describe, and extend growing patterns.

Listen and Draw

Use ▣ to show the number pattern 2, 4, 6, 8, 10.
Draw your cube towers.

HOME CONNECTION • In this activity, your child used cubes to represent a growing pattern.

Math Talk

Describe the cube towers you built.

What comes next in the growing pattern?

Each step has 2 more squares than the last step. The squares are added to the side.

Describe how the pattern is growing. Trace what comes next in the pattern.

Share and Show MATH BOARD

Draw what comes next in the pattern.

1.

_____

☑2.

_____

☑3.

_____

Name _____

Draw what comes next in the pattern.

4.

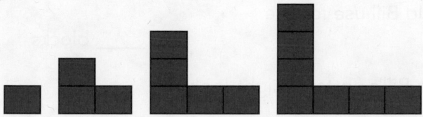

_____

5.

_____

6.

_____

7.

_____

8

 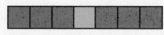

_____

Problem Solving • Applications  WRITE Math

9. **GO DEEPER** Bill uses blocks to make a pattern. He uses 2 blocks for the 1st step, 4 blocks for the 2nd step, and 6 blocks for the 3rd step. How many blocks should Bill use for the 5th step?

_____ blocks

Draw a picture of what Bill's pattern might look like.

Describe how the pattern is growing.

_____

_____

10. **THINK SMARTER** Tina made a pattern with stickers. How many stickers should she use for the next step in the pattern?

○ 4

○ 5

○ 7

○ 10

 TAKE HOME ACTIVITY • Use small objects, such as buttons, to make a growing pattern. Ask your child to describe how the pattern grows.

Algebra • Growing Patterns

Draw what comes next in the pattern.

Learning Objective You will identify, describe, and extend growing patterns.

1.

_____

2.
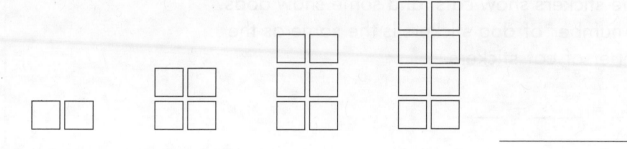
_____

3.

_____

Problem Solving

Solve. Draw to explain.

4. Ms. Lennox is building a display of stacked soup cans in her store. Draw what comes next in the pattern.

Lesson Check

1. Draw what comes next in the pattern.

_____

Spiral Review

2. Write a doubles fact to solve. Noah has 16 stickers.
   Some stickers show cats, and some show dogs.
   The number of dog stickers is the same as the
   number of cat stickers.

   _____ = _____ + _____

3. What comes next in this pattern?

 _____ _____

4. Count by tens.
   Write the missing numbers.

   4, 14, 24, _____, _____, 54

Name _____

Algebra • Transfer Patterns

Essential Question How can you show the same pattern in another way?

Learning Objective You will show the same repeating pattern or growing pattern in another way.

Listen and Draw

Use two shapes to draw a pattern core.
Repeat the pattern core three times.

Math Talk
How is your pattern core different from a classmate's pattern core?

HOME CONNECTION • In this activity, your child makes a repeating pattern using familiar shapes.

Show the same repeating pattern in another way.
Use numbers.

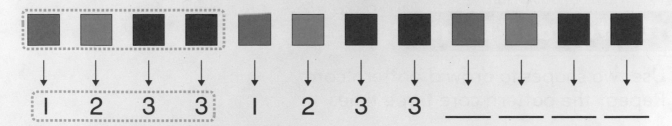

| 1 | 2 | 3 | 3 | 1 | 2 | 3 | 3 | ___ | ___ | ___ | ___ |

Show the same growing pattern in another way. Use numbers.

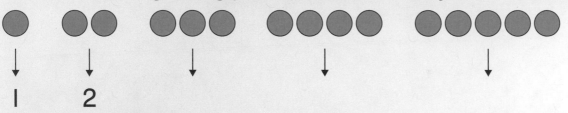

| 1 | 2 | ___ | ___ | ___ |

Show the same repeating pattern in another way.
Use numbers or pictures.

☑ 1.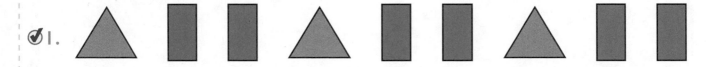

___ ___ ___ ___ ___ ___ ___ ___ ___

Show the same growing pattern in another way.
Use numbers or pictures.

☑ 2.

___ ___ ___ ___

Name _____

Show the same repeating pattern in another way.
Use numbers or pictures.

3.

_____ _____ _____ _____ _____ _____ _____ _____ _____

4.
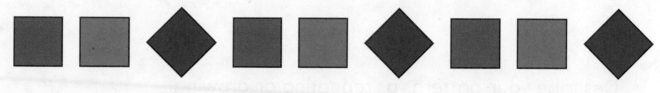

_____ _____ _____ _____ _____ _____ _____ _____ _____

Show the same growing pattern in another way.
Use numbers or pictures.

5.
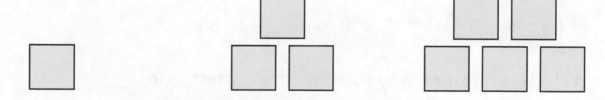

_____ _____ _____

6. **GO DEEPER**

2   3   4   5

_____ _____ _____

Problem Solving • Applications    WRITE Math

7. **GO DEEPER** Draw a shapes pattern.
Use four shapes in the pattern core.
Repeat the pattern core two times.
Then use numbers or pictures to show
your pattern in another way.

Describe your patterns as repeating or growing.

_____

8. **THINK SMARTER** Austin made this pattern
with number cards.

| 1 | 2 | 3 | 1 | 2 | 3 | 1 | 2 | 3 |

Which is another way to show the pattern core
for Austin's pattern?

 TAKE HOME ACTIVITY • With your child, draw a shapes pattern
with a pattern core made with three shapes. Repeat the pattern core
at least two times. Then use numbers or pictures to show the pattern in
another way.

Algebra • Transfer Patterns

Learning Objective You will show the same repeating pattern or growing pattern in another way.

Show the same repeating pattern in another way. Use numbers or pictures.

1.

___ ___ ___ ___ ___ ___ ___ ___ ___

2. ◇ ▯ ◇ ◇ ▯ ◇ ◇ ▯ ◇

___ ___ ___ ___ ___ ___ ___ ___ ___

Show the same growing pattern in another way.
Use numbers or pictures.

3.   2   4   6   8

_____ _____ _____ _____

Problem Solving

4. Draw shapes to make a pattern. Then use numbers or pictures to show your pattern in another way.

Lesson Check

1. Show the same repeating pattern in another way.
   Use numbers or pictures.

___ ___ ___ ___ ___ ___ ___ ___ ___

Spiral Review

2. What number does the model
   show? Write the number.

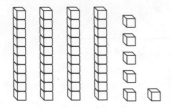

_____ tens _____ ones = _____

3. Write two subtraction facts
   related to 6 + 4 = 10.

   ____ – ____ = ____

   ____ – ____ = ____

4. Draw what comes next in the growing pattern.

_____

Algebra • Skip Count on a Counting Chart

Learning Objective You will skip count by twos, fives, and tens on a Counting Chart.

Skip count. Show the pattern on the Counting Chart.

1. Count by fives. Circle the numbers.

2. Count by tens. Put an X on the numbers.

3. Start at 34. Count by twos. Write the numbers.

34, ____, ____, ____, ____, ____, ____

1	2	3	4	5	6	7	8	9	10
11	12	13	14	15	16	17	18	19	20
21	22	23	24	25	26	27	28	29	30
31	32	33	34	35	36	37	38	39	40
41	42	43	44	45	46	47	48	49	50
51	52	53	54	55	56	57	58	59	60
61	62	63	64	65	66	67	68	69	70
71	72	73	74	75	76	77	78	79	80
81	82	83	84	85	86	87	88	89	90
91	92	93	94	95	96	97	98	99	100
101	102	103	104	105	106	107	108	109	110
111	112	113	114	115	116	117	118	119	120

Problem Solving

4. Felix counts backward by tens. He starts on 120. Which of the following numbers will he say? Circle the numbers.

20   51   50   88   110   81   70   40   57

Lesson Check

1. What number is next in the skip counting pattern 26, 28, 30, 32, _____?

_____

1	2	3	4	5	6	7	8	9	10
11	12	13	14	15	16	17	18	19	20
21	22	23	24	25	26	27	28	29	30
31	32	33	34	35	36	37	38	39	40
41	42	43	44	45	46	47	48	49	50

Spiral Review

2. Which number is odd?
   - ○ 10
   - ○ 18
   - ○ 24
   - ○ 27

3. Which number is even?
   - ○ 9
   - ○ 13
   - ○ 22
   - ○ 41

4. Write the number four hundred thirty-three with digits.

_____

5. Charles is the seventeenth person in line. How many people are in front of him?

_____ people

Name _____

Equal and Not Equal Amounts

Essential Question How do you know if the two sides of a number sentence are equal or not equal?

Learning Objective You will use = or ≠ to show if the two sides of a number sentence are equal or not equal.

Listen and Draw **Hands On**

Use cubes to model the problem.
Then draw to show your work.

FOR THE TEACHER • Read the following problems. Have children solve and explain their answers. • Alana has 6 red buttons and 4 blue buttons. Teresa has 8 green buttons and 2 black buttons. Do Alana and Teresa have the same number of buttons? Explain. • Ross has 8 red buttons and 5 blue buttons. Grant has 6 green buttons and 5 black buttons. Do Ross and Grant have the same number of buttons? Explain.

Math Talk
Explain how you can compare the number of buttons that the boys in the second problem have.

Use = to show that two amounts are equal. 5 = 5

Use ≠ to show that two amounts are **not equal**. 5 ≠ 4

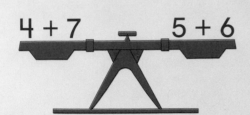

4 + 7   5 + 6

4 + 7   5 + 6

11 (=) 11

So, 4 + 7 = 5 + 6.

is equal to

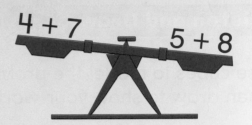

4 + 7   5 + 8

4 + 7   5 + 8

11 (≠) 13

So, 4 + 7 ≠ 5 + 8.

is not equal to

Share and Show

Write = or ≠ to make the number sentence true.

1. 8 + 5 ◯ 6 + 7   2. 5 + 8 ◯ 9 + 6

3. 11 − 4 ◯ 14 − 6   4. 10 − 5 ◯ 5

⊘ 5. 9 + 0 ◯ 4 + 5   ⊘ 6. 15 − 6 ◯ 9 − 3

Name _____

Write = or ≠ to make the number sentence true.

7. 6 + 8 ◯ 7 + 5

8. 5 + 7 ◯ 12

9. 9 + 5 ◯ 7 + 7

10. 16 − 7 ◯ 17 − 9

11. 12 ◯ 6 + 5

12. 9 + 5 ◯ 5 + 9

13. 6 + 4 ◯ 10 + 0

14. 12 − 5 ◯ 14 − 7

15. 9 + 4 ◯ 6 + 7

16. 12 − 8 ◯ 11 − 7

GO DEEPER Write a number to make the number sentence true.

17. 4 + 7 ≠ 5 + ☐

18. 4 + 5 = 12 − ☐

19. 14 − 6 = 4 + ☐

20. 8 + 2 ≠ 6 + ☐

21. 16 − 7 ≠ 6 + ☐

22. 13 − 5 = 14 − ☐

Problem Solving • Applications WRITE Math

Circle all the cards that make the number sentence true.

23.

☐ = 12

| $5 + 2 + 5$ | $6 + 5$ |
| $8 + 4$ | $7 + 3 + 3$ |

24. GO DEEPER

☐ ≠ 9

| $18 - 9$ | $13 - 5$ |
| $3 + 3 + 6$ | $16 - 7$ |

25.

☐ = 15

| $9 + 6$ | $7 + 8$ |
| $8 + 9$ | $4 + 2 + 5$ |

26. THINK SMARTER Marisa wrote a number sentence on the board.

$13 - 6 \neq$ ☁

Which makes this number sentence true?

- ○ $3 + 4$
- ○ $14 - 8$
- ○ $7 + 0$
- ○ $16 - 9$

 TAKE HOME ACTIVITY • Ask your child to tell you what the symbol ≠ means and then complete this number sentence. $3 + 8 \neq$ __.

Name _____

Equal and Not Equal Amounts

Write = or ≠ to make the number sentence true.

Learning Objective You will use = or ≠ to show if the two sides of a number sentence are equal or not equal.

1. $4 + 2 \bigcirc 5 + 1$

2. $7 + 5 \bigcirc 6 + 6$

3. $15 - 6 \bigcirc 16 - 7$

4. $8 + 4 \bigcirc 9 + 2$

5. $8 - 1 \bigcirc 11 - 3$

6. $12 - 5 \bigcirc 10 - 3$

7. $9 + 0 \bigcirc 0 + 9$

8. $7 + 2 \bigcirc 6 + 5$

9. $10 - 4 \bigcirc 9 - 5$

10. $14 - 7 \bigcirc 6 + 1$

11. $9 + 6 \bigcirc 8 + 6$

12. $7 - 3 \bigcirc 2 + 2$

Problem Solving

13. Circle all the cards that make the number sentence true.

$\boxed{} = 14$

| $5 + 4 + 5$ | $7 + 7$ |
| $9 + 5$ | $7 + 9$ |

Lesson Check

1. Write = or ≠ to make the number sentence true.

    $7 + 4 \bigcirc 10 + 2$

2. Write = or ≠ to make the number sentence true.

    $12 - 6 \bigcirc 10 - 4$

Spiral Review

3. Write the number that is 10 less than 458.

    _____

4. What is the value of the underlined digit?

    6̲14

    _____

5. Billy made this pattern with shapes. What is the next shape in the pattern?

Name _____

Compare Using Symbols and Words

Essential Question How can you use symbols and words to compare numbers?

Learning Objective You will use symbols and words to compare numbers.

Listen and Draw Hands On

Use ▭▭▭▭▭ ▪. Draw quick pictures to show your work. Write the numbers to compare.

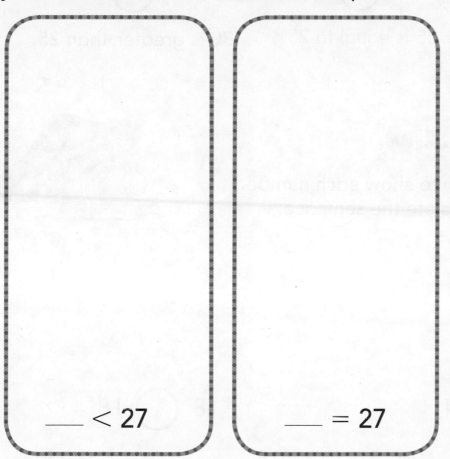

_____ < 27

_____ = 27

_____ > 27

FOR THE TEACHER • Have children use base-ten blocks to show a number less than 27, a number equal to 27, and a number greater than 27.

Math Talk

Compare 39 and 24 in two ways. What two symbols will you use? **Explain.**

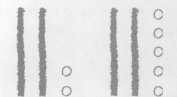 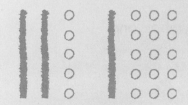 

22 (<) 25

22 is less than 25.

25 (=) 25

25 is equal to 25.

30 (>) 25

30 is greater than 25.

Share and Show MATH BOARD

Use [illustration]. Draw to show each number.
Write <, >, or =. Complete the sentence.

1.

27 ◯ 34

27 _____ 34.

2.

18 ◯ 18

18 _____ 18.

 3.

47 ◯ 33

47 _____ 33.

☑ 4.

50 ◯ 51

50 _____ 51.

Name _____

Write <, >, or =. Complete the sentence.
Draw a quick picture if you need to.

REMEMBER
< is less than
> is greater than
= is equal to

5.

44 ◯> 41

44 ___is greater than___ 41.

6.

37 ◯ 50

37 _____ 50.

7.

56 ◯ 56

56 _____ 56.

8.

62 ◯ 72

62 _____ 72.

9.

70 ◯ 65

70 _____ 65.

10.

93 ◯ 90

93 _____ 90.

 GO DEEPER Write numbers to solve.

11.

98 = ___

12.

43 > ___

13.

85 < ___

Problem Solving • Applications

Solve. Write or draw to explain.

14. There are 56 pages in Keisha's notebook. There are 58 pages in Jack's notebook. Whose notebook has more pages?

_____ notebook

15. **GO DEEPER** Ms. Bradford sees more than 79 birds but fewer than 92 birds. How many birds might she have seen?

_____ birds

16. **THINK SMARTER** Which is true?

○ 21 > 28

○ 21 = 28

○ 21 < 28

○ 28 < 21

 TAKE HOME ACTIVITY • Ask your child how he or she compares numbers, such as 85 and 78.

Compare Using Symbols and Words

Learning Objective You will use symbols and words to compare numbers.

Write $<$, $>$, or $=$. Complete the sentence.
Draw a quick picture if you need to.

1.

37 ◯ 30

37 _____ 30.

2.

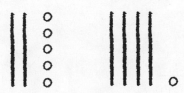

25 ◯ 41

25 _____ 41.

3.

41 ◯ 50

41 _____ 50.

4.

70 ◯ 70

70 _____ 70.

5.

99 ◯ 98

99 _____ 98.

6.

85 ◯ 58

85 _____ 58.

Problem Solving · Real World

Write $<$, $>$, or $=$ to solve. Circle your answer.

7. Sandy has 43 pennies. Zara has 46 pennies.
Who has a greater number of pennies?

46 ◯ 43   Sandy   Zara

Lesson Check

1. Write the symbol that means **is less than**.

   ____

2. Write a number to solve.

   $92 = $ ____

Spiral Review

3. What is the value of the underlined digit?

   3<u>8</u>2

   _____

4. Write the number that is 100 more than 612.

   _____

5. Show the same pattern in another way.
   Use numbers or pictures.

   _____

Name _____

Algebra • Order Numbers

Essential Question How do you order numbers?

Learning Objective You will order three-digit numbers from least to greatest and from greatest to least.

Listen and Draw Real World

Write the numbers. Then draw quick pictures.

Hundreds	Tens	Ones

_____ red stars

Hundreds	Tens	Ones

_____ blue stars

Hundreds	Tens	Ones

_____ green stars

FOR THE TEACHER • Read the following sentences. • Kwan has three groups of stars. He has 251 red stars, 97 blue stars, and 236 green stars. Have children write the numbers and then draw quick pictures.

Math Talk
Explain how the numbers are different.

Model and Draw

You can compare digits to order numbers from least to greatest or from greatest to least.

147   142   145

2 < 5 < 7   7 > 5 > 2

142 ◯ 145 ◯ 147
least   greatest

_____ ◯ _____ ◯ _____
greatest   least

Share and Show

Write the number for each model first.

Compare the numbers. Write them in order from least to greatest. Write > or <.

1.

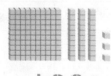 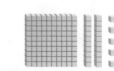

133

_____ ◯ _____ ◯ _____
least   greatest

2.

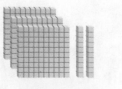 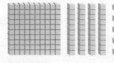

_____ ◯ _____ ◯ _____
least   greatest

Name _____

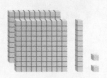
Compare the numbers. Write them in order from greatest to least. Write > or <.

Write the number for each model first.

3.

_____   ○   _____   ○   _____
greatest   least

4.
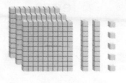 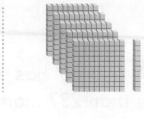

_____   ○   _____   ○   _____
greatest   least

 Compare the numbers to solve.

5.   865
       705
       895
       645

Which is greatest? _____

Which is least? _____

6.   790
       89
       776
       812

Which is greatest? _____

Which is least? _____

Problem Solving • Applications  Math

Solve.

7. There are 3 trucks carrying oranges. One truck has 450 oranges. Another truck has 540 oranges, and the other truck has 514 oranges.

Label the trucks in order of greatest number to least number of oranges.

greatest   least

8. **GO DEEPER** Paul has fewer than 305 stamps. He has more than 237 stamps. How many stamps might he have? Write that number in the box.

305 > ☐ > 237

9. **THINK SMARTER** Mrs. Lewis has 582 craft sticks. Mr. Johnson has 579 craft sticks. Mrs. Burman has 591 craft sticks. Which of the following is true?

○ 579 < 591 < 582   ○ 582 > 579 > 591

○ 591 < 579 < 582   ○ 591 > 582 > 579

 TAKE HOME ACTIVITY • Write three 3-digit numbers. Then have your child write the numbers in order from least to greatest.

Algebra • Order Numbers

Compare the numbers. Write them in order from greatest to least. Write > or <.

Learning Objective You will order three-digit numbers from least to greatest and from greatest to least.

1.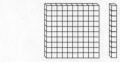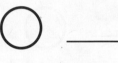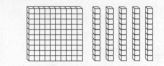

   _____   _____   _____

   _____ ◯ _____ ◯ _____
   greatest   least

2.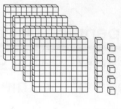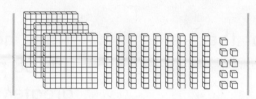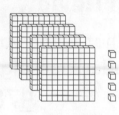

   _____   _____   _____

   _____ ◯ _____ ◯ _____
   greatest   least

Problem Solving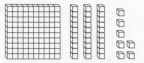

3. Maurice has more than 554 cards. He has fewer than 592 cards. How many cards might he have? Write that number in the box.

   554 < [____] < 592

Lesson Check

1. Compare the numbers. Write them in order from least to greatest. Write > or <.

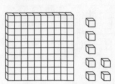 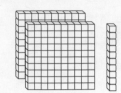 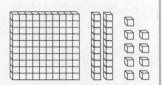

_____   _____   _____

_____ ◯ _____ ◯ _____
least   greatest

Spiral Review

2. What is the value of the underlined digit?

   <u>4</u>78

   _____

3. Tiana has 65 pennies. Joseph has 68 pennies. Who has a greater number of pennies? Circle the answer.

   Tiana   Joseph

4. Which makes the number sentence true?

   14 − 7 = _____

   ○ 6 + 1
   ○ 10 − 4
   ○ 5 + 3
   ○ 12 − 3

5. Which number is 100 more than 523?

   ○ 423
   ○ 524
   ○ 533
   ○ 623

Name _____

Estimate Sums

Essential Question How can you estimate sums?

Listen and Draw Real World

Draw quick pictures for the numbers.

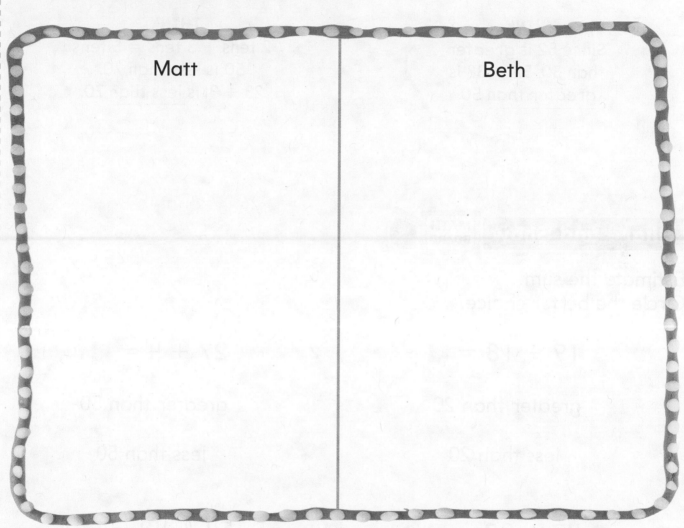

Matt

Beth

Matt and Beth have _____ than 20 crayons.

FOR THE TEACHER • Read the following problem. Have children draw quick pictures to represent the numbers and then answer the question. • Matt has 9 crayons and Beth has 7 crayons. Together, do they have more or less than 20 crayons?

Math Talk
Explain how you could answer the question without finding the exact number of crayons.

Model and Draw

When you **estimate**, you tell about how many.

Estimate. Is the sum greater or less than 50?

$$52 + 38 = \blacksquare$$

THINK:
Since 52 is greater than 50, 52 + 38 is greater than 50.

Estimate. Is the sum greater or less than 70?

$$23 + 31 = \blacksquare$$

THINK:
2 tens + 3 tens = 5 tens
50 is less than 70.
23 + 31 is less than 70.

Share and Show

Estimate the sum.
Circle the better choice.

1. $19 + 18 = \blacksquare$

   greater than 20

   less than 20

2. $27 + 4 = \blacksquare$

   greater than 50

   less than 50

✓ 3. $47 + 32 = \blacksquare$

   greater than 50

   less than 50

✓ 4. $54 + 43 = \blacksquare$

   greater than 70

   less than 70

On Your Own

Estimate the sum.
Circle the better choice.

5. $11 + 0 = \blacksquare$

greater than 20

less than 20

6. $50 + 43 = \blacksquare$

greater than 50

less than 50

7. $35 + 33 = \blacksquare$

greater than 50

less than 50

8. $31 + 34 = \blacksquare$

greater than 70

less than 70

9. $16 + 32 = \blacksquare$

greater than 20

less than 20

10. $3 + 7 = \blacksquare$

greater than 20

less than 20

11. $24 + 40 = \blacksquare$

greater than 70

less than 70

12. $71 + 16 = \blacksquare$

greater than 70

less than 70

Problem Solving   WRITE Math

Estimate to solve.

13. **GO DEEPER** Vanessa says she has more than 70 stickers.
She has 20 bird stickers, 20 puppy stickers, and
25 kitten stickers. Is Vanessa's answer reasonable?
Explain.

_____

_____

_____

14. Estimate which is greater,
the number of roses in the
garden, or the total number
of daisies and violets. Circle
to show the answer.

Flowers in the Garden	
Flowers	Number of Flowers
daisies	37
roses	50
violets	21

roses   daisies and violets

15. **THINK SMARTER** Mr. Ortega has some paper clips.
He has 47 large paper clips and 36 small paper clips.
He estimates that he has more than 50 paper clips.
Is Mr. Ortega's estimate reasonable? Explain.

_____

_____

_____

 TAKE HOME ACTIVITY • Have your child explain how
he or she solved Exercise 14.

Name _____

Estimate Sums

Learning Objective You will estimate the sum of two addends.

Estimate the sum.
Circle the better choice.

1. 24 + 35 = ■

   greater than 70

   less than 70

2. 23 + 35 = ■

   greater than 50

   less than 50

3. 21 + 18 = ■

   greater than 20

   less than 20

4. 19 + 27 = ■

   greater than 20

   less than 20

5. 86 + 13 = ■

   greater than 70

   less than 70

6. 13 + 21 = ■

   greater than 50

   less than 50

7. 45 + 35 = ■

   greater than 50

   less than 50

8. 50 + 10 = ■

   greater than 70

   less than 70

9. 4 + 6 = ■

   greater than 20

   less than 20

Problem Solving

10. In the store, there are 40 goldfish, 31 clownfish, and 38 angelfish.
    Estimate the total number of clownfish and angelfish. Circle the better choice.

    greater than 50

    less than 50

Lesson Check

1. Circle the best estimate for the sum.

$$18 + 23 = \blacksquare$$

less than 20

less than 50

greater than 50

greater than 70

2. Circle the best estimate for the sum.

$$39 + 54 = \blacksquare$$

less than 20

less than 50

greater than 50

greater than 70

Spiral Review

3. Write the number that is 10 less than 347.

_____

4. Circle the odd number.

4   8

13   16

5. What number is next in the skip counting pattern 25, 30, 35, 40, ___ ?

_____

1	2	3	4	5	6	7	8	9	10
11	12	13	14	15	16	17	18	19	20
21	22	23	24	25	26	27	28	29	30
31	32	33	34	35	36	37	38	39	40
41	42	43	44	45	46	47	48	49	50

Name _____

Estimate Differences

Essential Question How can you estimate a difference?

Learning Objective You will estimate differences of 2-digit numbers.

Listen and Draw *Real World*

Label the number line. Circle the number in the problem.

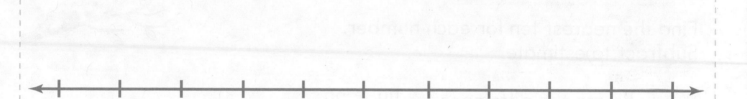

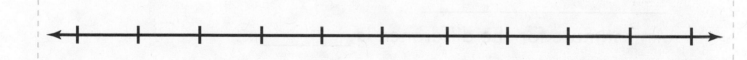

 FOR THE TEACHER • Read the following problem. • Between which two tens is 27? Children should label the endpoints of the first number line with the two tens, label the other numbers, and circle 27. Repeat the activity for 52 and 36.

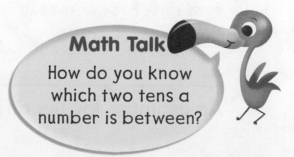 **Math Talk**
How do you know which two tens a number is between?

Virginia SOL Success • 5.2a

Estimate the difference for 63 − 48.
Find the nearest ten for each number.

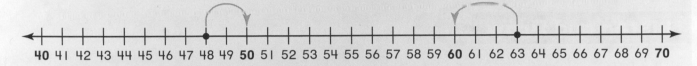

40 41 42 43 44 45 46 47 **48** 49 **50** 51 52 53 54 55 56 57 58 59 **60** 61 62 **63** 64 65 66 67 68 69 **70**

$$60 - 50 = 10$$

An estimate for the difference is __10__.

Share and Show

Find the nearest ten for each number.
Subtract to estimate.

1. Estimate the difference for 44 − 29.

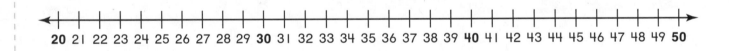

20 21 22 23 24 25 26 27 28 **29** **30** 31 32 33 34 35 36 37 38 39 **40** 41 42 43 44 45 46 47 48 49 **50**

_____

An estimate for the difference is _____.

2. Estimate the difference for 77 − 53.

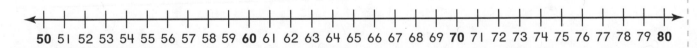

50 51 52 **53** 54 55 56 57 58 59 **60** 61 62 63 64 65 66 67 68 69 **70** 71 72 73 74 75 76 **77** 78 79 **80**

_____

An estimate for the difference is _____.

Name _____

On Your Own

Find the nearest ten for each number.
Subtract to estimate.

3. Estimate the difference for 54 − 37.

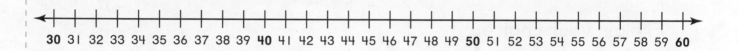

_____

An estimate for the difference is _____.

4. Estimate the difference for 79 − 56.

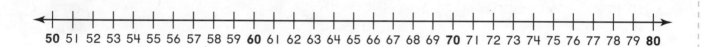

_____

An estimate for the difference is _____.

5. Estimate the difference for 93 − 78.

_____

An estimate for the difference is _____.

Problem Solving • Applications    Math

6. **GO DEEPER** Monica needs to estimate the difference for 84 − 22. Circle the estimate that you think is reasonable.

$$100 - 20 = 80 \qquad 80 - 20 = 60 \qquad 70 - 30 = 40$$

Explain your choice.

_____

_____

7. At the store, there are 94 apples and 68 pears. Estimate how many more apples than pears are at the store.

about _____ more apples

8. **THINK SMARTER** Samantha has 72 marbles. Julian has 43 marbles. Samantha estimates that she has about 30 more marbles than Julian. Is Samantha's estimate reasonable? Explain.

_____

_____

_____

_____

TAKE HOME ACTIVITY • Have your child explain how he or she solved Exercise 7.

Estimate Differences

Find the nearest ten for each number. Subtract to estimate.

Learning Objective You will estimate differences of 2-digit numbers.

1. Estimate the difference for 48 − 21.

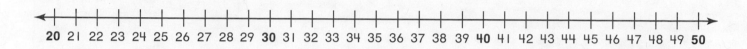

20 21 22 23 24 25 26 27 28 29 **30** 31 32 33 34 35 36 37 38 39 **40** 41 42 43 44 45 46 47 48 49 **50**

_____

An estimate for the difference is _____.

2. Estimate the difference for 54 − 38.

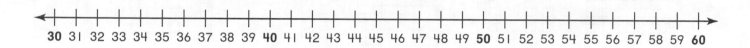

30 31 32 33 34 35 36 37 38 39 **40** 41 42 43 44 45 46 47 48 49 **50** 51 52 53 54 55 56 57 58 59 **60**

_____

An estimate for the difference is _____.

Problem Solving

Solve. Write or draw to explain.

3. Isaac has 53 pennies. Rachel has 94 pennies. Estimate how many more pennies Rachel has than Isaac.

about _____ more pennies

Lesson Check

1. Estimate the difference for 78 − 51.

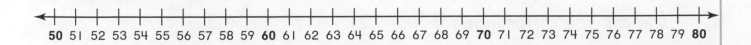

50 51 52 53 54 55 56 57 58 59 **60** 61 62 63 64 65 66 67 68 69 **70** 71 72 73 74 75 76 77 78 79 **80**

_____

Spiral Review

Compare the numbers. Write them in order
from greatest to least. Write > or <.

2.

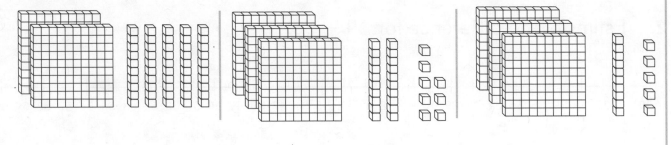

_____   _____   _____

_____ ◯ _____ ◯ _____
greatest   least

---

3. What is the value of the
underlined digit?

7̲58

_____

4. Carmela is the twentieth
person in line. How many
people are in line in front
of her?

_____ people

Name _____

Create and Solve Practical Problems

Essential Question How can you create and solve two-step addition and subtraction word problems?

Learning Objective You will create and solve two-step word problems.

Listen and Draw

Listen to the word problem.
Draw quick pictures to show the numbers.
Then solve each problem.

$$18 + 22 = \underline{\hspace{2cm}}$$

There are _____ flowers in all.

$$52 - 25 = \underline{\hspace{2cm}}$$

Mrs. Lopez now has _____ strawberries.

 FOR THE TEACHER • Read the following problems. Have children draw quick pictures to represent the numbers and solve the problems. • There are 18 roses and 22 tulips in Jan's garden. How many flowers are there in all? • Mrs. Lopez bought 52 strawberries. She uses 25 of the strawberries to make a pie. How many strawberries does she have now?

 Math Talk Math Processes and Practices ❶

How do quick pictures help you solve each problem?

Model and Draw

You can create and solve a two-step word problem.
Use the number sentences. Draw quick pictures to solve.

Ben has 17 blue marbles and 28 multi-color marbles.

$17 + 28 = \underline{45}$

Step 1:
Write a word problem for the first number sentence. Draw quick pictures. Add.

He gives his sister 20 of his marbles. How many marbles does Ben have now?

$45 - 20 = \underline{25}$

Ben has _____ marbles now.

Step 2:
Continue the word problem for the second number sentence. Draw quick pictures. Subtract.

Share and Show   MATH BOARD

☑ 1. Write a two-step word problem for the number sentences. Draw quick pictures to solve.

$20 + 20 = \underline{\hspace{1.5cm}}$

_____

_____

 $\underline{\hspace{1cm}} + 29 = 69$

_____

Remember to continue the story in the word problem.

Name _____

On Your Own

2. Write two-step word problems for the number sentences. Draw quick pictures to solve.

$$25 + 30 = \underline{\hspace{2cm}}$$

_____

_____

_____

$$81 - \underline{\hspace{2cm}} = 26$$

_____

_____

_____

3.  Write and solve a two-step word problem. Use the numbers 42, 78, and 36.

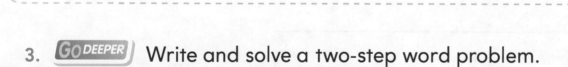

_____ + _____ = _____
_____ − _____ = _____

_____

_____

_____

_____

Problem Solving • Applications  WRITE Math

4. The number sentences show two steps used to solve a problem. Write a two-step problem that can be solved by using the number sentences.

$$21 + 42 = 63$$

_____

_____

_____

_____

$$63 + 12 = 75$$

_____

_____

_____

_____

5. **THINK SMARTER** Explain how to write a two-step word problem.

_____

_____

_____

 TAKE HOME ACTIVITY • Have your child draw pictures to represent 11 − 7 = ____ and 4 + 6 = ____. Then have him or her write a two-step word problem for the number sentences.

Create and Solve Practical Problems

Learning Objective You will create and solve two-step word problems.

1. Write two-step word problems for the number sentences. Draw quick pictures to solve.

   $36 + 23 =$ _____

   _____

   _____

   _____

   $59 -$ _____ $= 15$

   _____

   _____

   _____

Problem Solving Real World

2. Write a two-step word problem. Make one step addition and one step subtraction. Write a number sentence for each step. Draw quick pictures to solve.

   _____

   _____

   _____

3. **WRITE** Math How do quick pictures help you solve a two-step problem?

   _____

   _____

Lesson Check

1. Write numbers to complete the two-step word problem.
   Then solve. Draw quick pictures if you like.

   Rob picked _____ apples.

   He gave _____ apples to Zoe.

   Then he picks _____ more apples.

   How many apples does Rob have now? _____ apples

Spiral Review

2. Estimate the sum. Circle the better choice.

   $$26 + 31 = \blacksquare$$

   greater than 50   less than 50

3. Label the bar model. Solve the word problem.

   Rajiv has 58 marbles in a blue box.

   Alicia has 29 fewer marbles than Rajiv.

   How many marbles does Alicia have?

   _____ marbles

Algebra • Compare Money Amounts

Essential Question How do you compare amounts of money?

Learning Objective You will compare amounts of money using words.

Listen and Draw Real World

Use coins to show the amounts.
Then draw the coins.

_____ is greater than _____.

FOR THE TEACHER • Distribute sets of mixed-value play coins. Have children show 32 cents in the first box and 35 cents in the second box. Then have children draw the coins they used and complete the comparison statement.

Math Talk

Compare 46¢ and 64¢. Use **is greater than** to tell about these amounts.

Virginia SOL Success • 7.6a

Model and Draw

Compare total values of groups of money.
Write **is greater than**, **is less than**, or **is equal to**.

Compare the dollars. Both amounts have the same
number of dollars. Then compare the cents. 25 > 15

$1.25 _____ $1.15.

Share and Show MATH BOARD

Write the total value of each group.
Then write **is greater than**, **is less than**, or **is equal to**.

☑ 1.

_____ _____ _____.

☑ 2.

_____ _____ _____.

On Your Own

Write the total value of each group.
Then write **is greater than**, **is less than**, or **is equal to**.

3.

_____ _____ _____ .

4.

_____ _____ _____ .

5.

_____ _____ _____ .

Problem Solving • Applications

Read the clues. Draw the money.

6. Jake has 3 coins.
   He has more than 55¢.
   What coins might Jake have?

   Jake's coins

7. Beth has 4 coins.
   She has no nickels or pennies.
   She has less than 60¢.
   What coins might Beth have?

   Beth's coins

8. **GO DEEPER** Luke has one $1 bill and 4 coins. He has no quarters or pennies. He has less than $1.40. He has more than $1.25. What coins might Luke have?

   Luke's coins

9. **THINK SMARTER** Sandra has these coins. Which group of coins has a greater value than Sandra's coins?

   ○ 30 pennies

   ○ 6 nickels

   ○ 3 dimes

   ○ 2 quarters

 TAKE HOME ACTIVITY • Draw two groups of money, each with a total value of less than $2.00. Have your child find the total value of each group and then compare the values.

Algebra • Compare Money Amounts

Write the total value of each group.
Then write **is greater than, is less than,**
or **is equal to**.

Learning Objective You will compare amounts of money using words.

1.

   ___ _____ ___.

2.

   ___ _____ ___.

3.

   ___ _____ ___.

Problem Solving *Real World*

Read the clues. Draw the coins.

4. Maya has 4 coins.
   She has no dimes or pennies.
   The total value of her coins is less than 65¢.
   Which coins might Maya have?

Lesson Check

1. Write the total value of each group. Then write
    is greater than, is less than or **is equal to.**

_____ _____ _____.

Spiral Review

2. The red box has 126 pencils.
    The blue box has 143 pencils.
    The yellow box has
    135 pencils. Which of the
    following is true?

    ○ 126 < 135 < 143

    ○ 135 < 143 < 126

    ○ 135 > 143 > 126

    ○ 143 > 126 > 135

3. Martha saved 342 pennies.
    Jake saved 219 pennies.
    Cody saved 275 pennies.
    Which of the following is true?

    ○ 219 < 342 < 275

    ○ 275 < 219 < 342

    ○ 342 > 275 > 219

    ○ 342 > 219 > 275

---

4. Estimate the difference for 53 – 34.

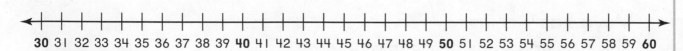

30 31 32 33 34 35 36 37 38 39 **40** 41 42 43 44 45 46 47 48 49 **50** 51 52 53 54 55 56 57 58 59 **60**

_____

Picture Graphs

Essential Question How does a key for a picture graph help you read the data?

Learning Objective You will read and represent data in picture graphs where each picture stands for more than one person, place, or thing.

Listen and Draw Real World

Take turns choosing a color tile from the bag. Draw a smiley face in the graph for each tile.

Tile Colors

green					
yellow					
red					
blue					

Key: Each ☺ stands for 1 tile.

Math Talk Math Processes and Practices ⑦

Explain how you know that the number of smiley faces for red matches the number of red tiles.

HOME CONNECTION • Your child made a graph by recording smiley faces for the colors of tiles taken from a bag. This activity prepares children for working with picture graphs in this lesson.

Model and Draw

A picture graph uses pictures to show information.
The key tells how many each picture stands for.

Number of Library Books Checked Out	
Name	**Tally**
Gwen	𝍩 𝍩
Tony	卌 卌 卌

Number of Library Books Checked Out			
Gwen	▪	▪	
Tony	▪	▪	▪

Key: Each ▪ stands for 5 books.

How many library books

did Tony check out? __15__ books

Skip Count: 5, 10, 15

Share and Show

MATH BOARD

Use the tally chart to complete the picture graph.
Draw a ☺ for every 2 children.

1.

Favorite Drink	
Drink	**Tally**
water	‖
juice	卌 ‖‖
milk	卌	

Favorite Drink				
water	☺			
juice				
milk				

Key: Each ☺ stands for 2 children.

✓ 2. How many children chose milk? _____ children

✓ 3. How many more children chose juice
than water? _____ more children

98 ninety-eight

© Houghton Mifflin Harcourt Publishing Company

Name ______________________________

On Your Own

4. Use the tally chart to complete the picture graph.
Draw a ☺ for every 2 children.

Favorite Planet

Planet	Tally
Mercury	IIII
Mars	II
Jupiter	𝍸 𝍸
Saturn	𝍸 III

Favorite Planet

Mercury					
Mars					
Jupiter					
Saturn					

Key: Each ☺ stands for 2 children.

5. How many children chose Mars? ______ children

6. How many fewer children chose Mercury than Jupiter? ______ fewer children

7. Which planet did the most children choose?

____

8. How many children in all chose a favorite planet? ______ children

9. GO DEEPER Look at the picture graph above.
Write about the information shown in this graph.

____

____

Problem Solving • Applications

Use the picture graph.

Favorite Color

red	☺	☺	☺	☺
blue	☺	☺	☺	
purple	☺			
green	☺	☺		

Key: Each ☺ stands for 2 children.

10. **GO DEEPER** Which two colors combined
were chosen by a total of 12 children? _____

11. **THINK SMARTER** Does the sentence describe the data
in the picture graph above? Choose Yes or No.

6 children chose blue.	○ Yes	○ No
More children chose green than red.	○ Yes	○ No
22 children chose a favorite color.	○ Yes	○ No
Red was chosen by the most children.	○ Yes	○ No

 TAKE HOME ACTIVITY • Have your child explain how
he or she solved one of the problems in this lesson.

Picture Graphs

Use the picture graph.

Learning Objective You will read and represent data in picture graphs where each picture stands for more than one person, place, or thing.

Favorite Month					
January	☺	☺			
April	☺	☺	☺		
August	☺	☺	☺	☺	☺
November	☺				

Key: Each ☺ stands for 2 children.

1. How many children chose January? _____ children

2. Which month did the fewest children choose? _____

3. How many children chose August? _____ children

4. How many more children chose April than January? _____ more children

Problem Solving

5. Suppose Jill draws another picture graph that shows the same data as the picture graph above. The key for her picture graph tells you that each smiley face stands for 10 children. How many smiley faces does Jill draw for August? Explain.

    _____

    _____

Lesson Check

1. Use the picture graph. Which 2 activities were chosen by the same number of children?

Favorite Outdoor Activity			
swimming	☺	☺	
running	☺		
biking	☺	☺	

_____

Key: Each ☺ stands for 5 children.

Spiral Review

2. Use the calendar. What is the date of the third Thursday in March?

   ○ March 9

   ○ March 15

   ○ March 16

   ○ March 23

March						
Sunday	Monday	Tuesday	Wednesday	Thursday	Friday	Saturday
			1	2	3	4
5	6	7	8	9	10	11
12	13	14	15	16	17	18
19	20	21	22	23	24	25
26	27	28	29	30	31	

3. There are 24 flowers in the vase. 18 of the flowers are yellow. How many flowers are not yellow?

   ○ 6

   ○ 14

   ○ 16

   ○ 42

4. Becky has 236 bird stickers and 173 fish stickers.

   Write a number sentence to show how many stickers Becky has in all.

   _____ + _____ = _____ stickers

Name _____

Compare and Contrast
Two-and Three-Dimensional Shapes

Essential Question What two-dimensional shapes do you see on the faces of three-dimensional shapes?

Learning Objective You will show how two-dimensional shapes and three-dimensional shapes are alike and different.

Listen and Draw

Draw to sort the shapes.

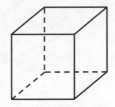

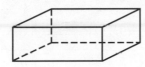

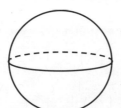

FOR THE TEACHER • Have children sort the shapes into two groups: two-dimensional shapes and three-dimensional shapes. Have them draw around each group to show how they sorted.

Math Talk
Math Processes and Practices **6**

Generalize Explain how you sorted the shapes.

© Houghton Mifflin Harcourt Publishing Company

Model and Draw

Trace around the faces of the
three-dimensional shape to find
the two-dimensional shapes.

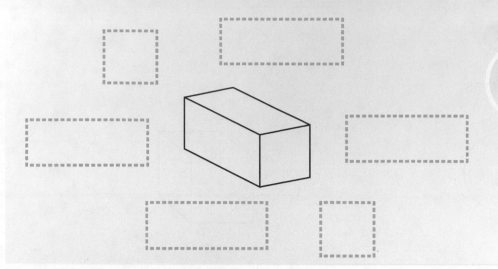

You draw four
rectangles and two
squares by tracing
around the faces
of the rectangular
prism.

Share and Show MATH BOARD

Use three-dimensional shapes. Trace around
the faces. Circle the shapes you draw.

✓1.

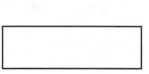

✓2.

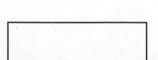

Name _____

Math Processes and Practices ⑥ **Make Connections** Circle the objects you could trace to draw the shape.

3.

4.

5.
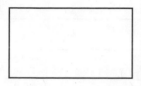

Circle the shape that the pattern will make if you fold it and tape it together.

6.
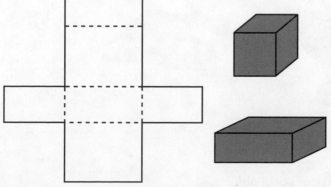

7.
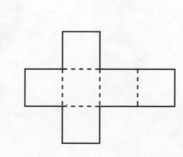

Problem Solving • Applications  WRITE Math

GO DEEPER Use three-dimensional shapes to solve the riddles. Circle the better choice.

8. I am a shape that can slide.
   I have 6 faces that are squares.
   Which shape am I?

9. I do not have a curved surface.
   I have 6 faces that are rectangles.
   Which shape am I?

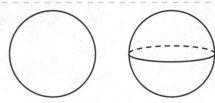

10. Look at the circle and the sphere.
    Describe how the shapes are alike
    and how they are different.

_____

_____

_____

11. **THINK SMARTER** Levi wants to trace a ▢. He finds these objects. Circle the object Levi should use.

 TAKE HOME ACTIVITY • Collect a few three-dimensional objects, such as boxes. Ask your child to identify the shapes of the faces of those objects.

Compare and Contrast Two-and Three-Dimensional Shapes

Learning Objective You will show how two-dimensional shapes and three-dimensional shapes are alike and different.

Circle the objects you could trace to draw the shape.

1.

2.

Problem Solving Real World

3. Look at this shape. Draw the shape you would make if you traced this object.

4. **WRITE Math** Use pictures or words to explain how you would describe the shapes of flat surfaces you may see on a tissue box.

Lesson Check

1. Which faces could a rectangular prism have?
   Circle the pair of shapes.

 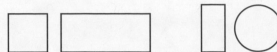

Spiral Review

2. Use the picture graph.
   How many more children chose baseball than soccer?

Our Favorite Sport

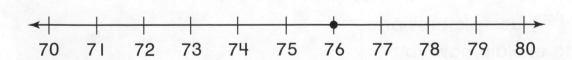

Key: Each 👤 **stands for 2 children.**

_____ more children

3. Round 76 to the nearest ten.

```
◄——+———+———+———+———+———+———●———+———+———+———►
    70   71   72   73   74   75   76   77   78   79   80
```

76 rounds to _____

Name _____

Unit Fractions of a Whole

Essential Question How can you identify unit fractions of a whole?

Learning Objective You will identify unit fractions of a whole.

 **Listen and Draw** Real World

Draw lines to show equal parts.

halves

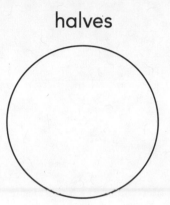

thirds

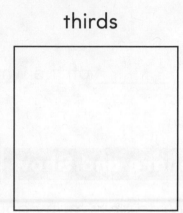

fourths

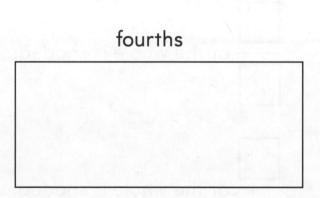

halves

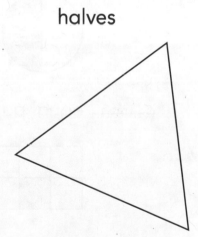

 HOME CONNECTION • Your child drew lines to show equal parts of different shapes and identified the equal parts of shapes as halves, thirds, and fourths. This will help your child develop an understanding of unit fractions.

Math Talk Math Processes and Practices ①

Explain how you know how to draw halves, thirds, and fourths.

Model and Draw

You can name a fraction when the whole is divided into equal parts.

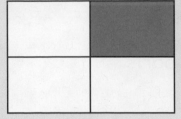

Think: 1 out of 4 equal parts
Say: one fourth

The top number tells how many parts are blue.
$$\frac{1}{4}$$
The bottom number tells how many equal parts are in the whole.

$\frac{1}{4}$ _____ of the whole is blue.

Share and Show MATH BOARD

Write how many equal parts there are.
Write the fraction that names the shaded part.

1.

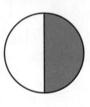

_____2_____ equal parts

$\dfrac{1}{2}$ _____ of the whole is shaded.

2.

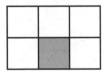

_____ equal parts

_____ of the whole is shaded.

3.

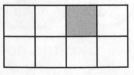

_____ equal parts

_____ of the whole is shaded.

Name _____

Write how many equal parts there are.
Write the fraction that names the shaded part.

4.

_____ equal parts

 of the whole is shaded.

5.

_____ equal parts

of the whole is shaded.

Color one part blue. Write the fraction that names the blue part.

6.

7.

8.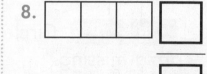

9. **GO DEEPER** Circle the picture that shows $\frac{1}{6}$. How did you know which picture to circle? Explain.

_____

_____

Problem Solving • Applications  Math

10. Anna cut a sheet of paper into 4 equal parts.
She gave one part to Josh. Color the part she gave to
Josh. Then write the fraction of paper she gave him.

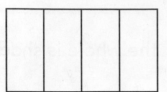

11. Use red to color $\frac{1}{3}$ of the shape that shows thirds.
Use blue to color $\frac{1}{4}$ of the shape that shows fourths.
Use green to color $\frac{1}{6}$ of the shape that shows sixths.
Use yellow to color $\frac{1}{8}$ of the shape that shows eighths.

12. **THINK SMARTER** Circle the picture that shows $\frac{1}{8}$ of the
pizza missing.

Explain how you knew which pizza to circle.

_____

_____

 TAKE HOME ACTIVITY • Fold a sheet of paper into six equal parts.
Then have your child shade one sixth of the paper.

Unit Fractions of a Whole

**Write how many equal parts there are.
Write the fraction that names the
shaded part.**

Learning Objective You will
identify unit fractions of a
whole.

1.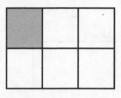

_____ equal parts

□/□ of the whole is shaded.

2.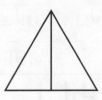

_____ equal parts

□/□ of the whole is shaded.

**Color one part red.
Write the fraction that names the red part.**

3.   □/□

4.   □/□

Problem Solving

5. Which is larger, $\frac{1}{3}$ of a pie or $\frac{1}{4}$ of the same size pie? Explain.

_____

_____

_____

Lesson Check

Draw and color to show the fraction.

1. $\frac{1}{3}$

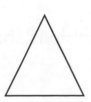

2. $\frac{1}{6}$

3. $\frac{1}{2}$

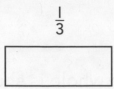

4. $\frac{1}{4}$

Spiral Review

5. Evan has a bag of blue and yellow tiles. The tally chart shows the color tiles Evan has pulled so far. Is the next tile Evan pulls more likely to be blue or yellow?

Tiles Evan Pulled	
Color	Tally
blue	卌 I
yellow	III

_____

6. Does the shape have a line of symmetry? Circle yes or no. If yes, draw the line.

yes   no

Name _____

Fraction Models

Essential Question How can you name and write fractions on a length model?

Learning Objective You will name and write fractions on a length model.

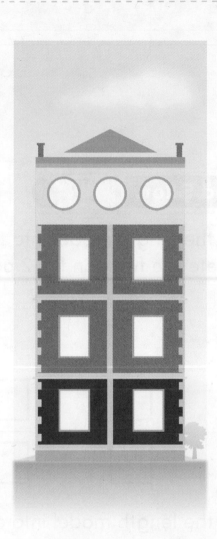

Math Talk Math Processes and Practices ❶

Explain how you can draw another line on the square windows to show fourths.

FOR THE TEACHER • Read the problem. • Draw to show equal parts. Draw lines on the square windows to show halves. Draw lines on the rectangle windows to show thirds. Draw lines on the circle windows to show fourths.

Model and Draw

Equal parts on a length model show fractions. This length model is divided into fourths.

What are the fractions for 1 part, 2 parts, and 3 parts?

$\frac{4}{4}$ is equal to 1 whole.

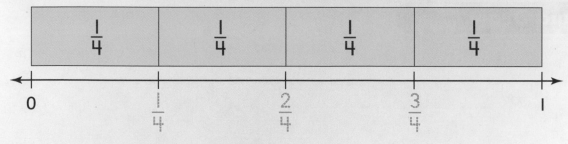

$\frac{1}{4}$ $\frac{1}{4}$ $\frac{1}{4}$ $\frac{1}{4}$

0      $\frac{1}{4}$ $\frac{2}{4}$ $\frac{3}{4}$ 1

Share and Show

1. Divide the length model into thirds.
   Complete the fraction for 2 parts.

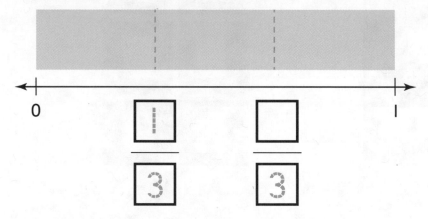

$\frac{}{3}$ $\frac{}{3}$

✔ 2. Divide the length model into eighths.
   Write the fraction for 5 parts.

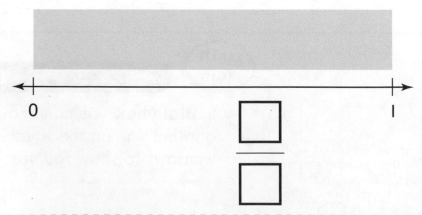

$\frac{}{}$

On Your Own

3. Divide the length model into halves.
   Write the fraction for 1 part.

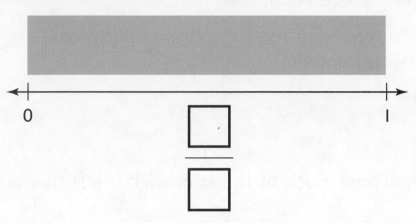

4. Divide the length model into sixths.
   Write the fraction for 4 parts.

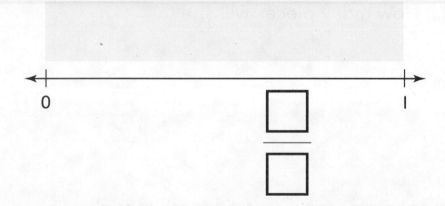

5. Divide the length model into fourths.
   Write the fraction for 3 parts.

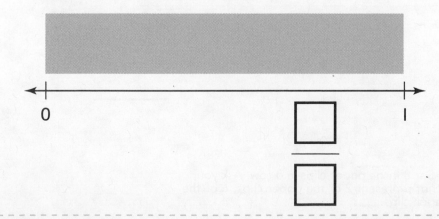

Problem Solving • Applications

6. Niko bought a submarine sandwich. He cut it into 6 equal pieces. He ate I piece and each of his 4 friends also ate I piece each.

   Draw a length model to represent the submarine sandwich. Shade the pieces that were eaten.

   Write a fraction to show how much of the sandwich is left over.

   _____ left over

7. **GO DEEPER** Nashi has two long boards. She needs 6 equal short boards. How many pieces will she cut each board into?

   _____ equal pieces

8. **THINK SMARTER** These paper clips represent a length model. Write the fraction for 2 paper clips.

   _____

 TAKE HOME ACTIVITY • Set 8 large paper clips in a row. Ask your child to name the fractions that represent 2 of the paper clips, 6 of the paper clips, and 8 of the paper clips.

Fraction Models

Learning Objective You will name and write fractions on a length model.

1. The length model is divided into _____.
   Write the fraction for 1 part.

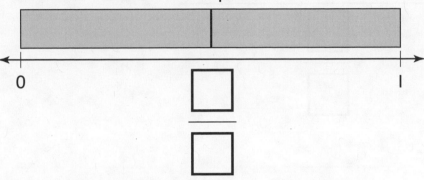

2. Divide the length model into eighths.
   Write the fractions for 3 parts and 7 parts.

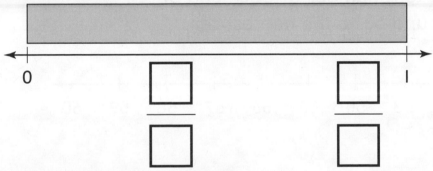

Problem Solving Real World

3. An unknown fraction is located on a length model exactly in the middle of $\frac{1}{4}$ and $\frac{3}{4}$. What is the unknown fraction?

   _____

4. **WRITE** Math Explain what the bottom number of a fraction tells.

   _____

   _____

Lesson Check

1. Divide the length model into thirds.
   Write the fractions for each part between 0 and 1.

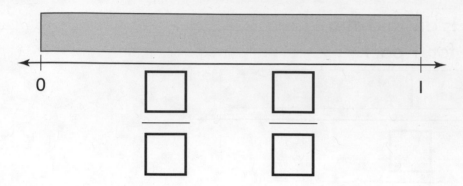

Spiral Review

2. Draw arrows to the tens number at each end of
   the number line. Round 53 to the nearest ten.

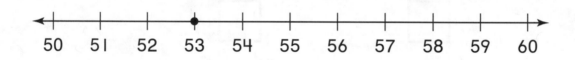

   53 rounds to _____.

3. Chris has a soccer game on the
   second Saturday in May.
   What date is his soccer game?

   _____

May						
Sunday	Monday	Tuesday	Wednesday	Thursday	Friday	Saturday
			1	2	3	4
5	6	7	8	9	10	11
12	13	14	15	16	17	18
19	20	21	22	23	24	25
26	27	28	29	30	31	

Name _____

Compare Unit Fractions

Essential Question How can you compare unit fractions using words and symbols?

Learning Objective You will compare unit fractions of a whole.

Listen and Draw

Color to show each fraction.

FOR THE TEACHER • Read the following problem. • Two fruit bars are the same size. Jeremy eats one third of one fruit bar. Nicole eats one half of the other fruit bar. Color the part of the bar Jeremy eats red. Color the part of the bar Nicole eats blue.

Math Talk Math Processes and Practices ❶

Explain how you know which fruit bar belongs to Jeremy and which belongs to Nicole.

Model and Draw

Compare $\frac{1}{4}$ and $\frac{1}{8}$.

THINK:
Which fraction strip shows more shading?

$\frac{1}{4}$ [fraction strip divided into 4 parts, first part shaded]

$\frac{1}{8}$ [fraction strip divided into 8 parts, first part shaded]

$\frac{1}{4}$ is greater than $\frac{1}{8}$. $\frac{1}{4} > \frac{1}{8}$

$\frac{1}{8}$ is less than $\frac{1}{4}$. $\frac{1}{8} < \frac{1}{4}$

Share and Show

Color the fraction strips to show the fractions.
Compare. Circle the greater fraction. Write > or < .

1. $\frac{1}{4}$ [fraction strip in 4 parts, first shaded]
   $\left(\frac{1}{2}\right)$ [fraction strip in 2 parts, first shaded]

   $\frac{1}{4}$ ◯ $\frac{1}{2}$
   $\frac{1}{2}$ ◯ $\frac{1}{4}$

2. $\frac{1}{3}$ [fraction strip in 3 parts, first shaded]
   $\frac{1}{6}$ [fraction strip in 6 parts, first shaded]

   $\frac{1}{3}$ ◯ $\frac{1}{6}$
   $\frac{1}{6}$ ◯ $\frac{1}{3}$

3. $\frac{1}{2}$ [fraction strip in 2 parts, first shaded]
   $\frac{1}{3}$ [fraction strip in 3 parts, first shaded]

   $\frac{1}{2}$ ◯ $\frac{1}{3}$
   $\frac{1}{3}$ ◯ $\frac{1}{2}$

Name _____

Color the fraction strips to show the fractions.
Compare. Circle the greater fraction. Write > or <.

4. $\frac{1}{8}$

$\frac{1}{2}$

$\frac{1}{8}$ ◯ $\frac{1}{2}$

$\frac{1}{2}$ ◯ $\frac{1}{8}$

5. $\frac{1}{3}$

$\frac{1}{6}$

$\frac{1}{3}$ ◯ $\frac{1}{6}$

$\frac{1}{6}$ ◯ $\frac{1}{3}$

6. $\frac{1}{3}$

$\frac{1}{4}$

$\frac{1}{3}$ ◯ $\frac{1}{4}$

$\frac{1}{4}$ ◯ $\frac{1}{3}$

7. $\frac{1}{6}$

$\frac{1}{8}$

$\frac{1}{6}$ ◯ $\frac{1}{8}$

$\frac{1}{8}$ ◯ $\frac{1}{6}$

8. **GO DEEPER** Color each square to show $\frac{1}{4}$. Compare.
Write >, <, or =.

$\frac{1}{4}$ ◯ $\frac{1}{4}$

Problem Solving • Applications WRITE Math

9. Two sandwiches are the same size. Mia eats $\frac{1}{2}$ of one sandwich. Lucas eats $\frac{1}{3}$ of the other sandwich. Who ate the larger part of their sandwich? Explain.

_____

_____

_____

10. Jake eats a piece of a pie that is $\frac{1}{4}$ of the pie. Alicia eats a smaller piece of the same pie. Circle the fractions of the pie Alicia might haven eaten.

$\frac{1}{6}$ $\frac{1}{2}$

$\frac{1}{3}$ $\frac{1}{8}$

11. **GO DEEPER** Mary has a slice of pizza that is $\frac{1}{4}$ of a pizza. Kim has a slice of pizza that is $\frac{1}{2}$ of a pizza. Kim's slice is smaller. Draw pizzas to show how this is possible.

How did you know how to draw the pizzas? Explain.

_____

_____

_____

12. **THINK SMARTER** Choose the unknown fraction.

$$\frac{1}{6} > \underline{\qquad}$$

$\frac{1}{3}$ ○ $\frac{1}{2}$ ○ $\frac{1}{8}$ ○ $\frac{1}{4}$ ○

 TAKE HOME ACTIVITY • Have your child exsplain how he or she solved Exercise 10.

Name _____

Compare Unit Fractions

Learning Objective You will compare unit fractions of a whole.

Color the fraction strips to show the fractions. Compare. Circle the greater fraction. Write > or <.

1. $\frac{1}{6}$

   $\frac{1}{2}$

   $\frac{1}{6}$ ◯ $\frac{1}{2}$

   $\frac{1}{2}$ ◯ $\frac{1}{6}$

2. $\frac{1}{3}$

   $\frac{1}{8}$

   $\frac{1}{3}$ ◯ $\frac{1}{8}$

   $\frac{1}{8}$ ◯ $\frac{1}{3}$

3. $\frac{1}{4}$

   $\frac{1}{6}$

   $\frac{1}{4}$ ◯ $\frac{1}{6}$

   $\frac{1}{6}$ ◯ $\frac{1}{4}$

Problem Solving

4. Divide each shape to show halves. Show two different ways. Color each shape to show $\frac{1}{2}$. Compare. Write >, < or =.

$\frac{1}{2}$ ◯ $\frac{1}{2}$

Lesson Check

Color the shapes to show the fractions.
Compare. Write >, <, or =.

1.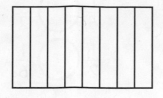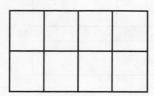

$\frac{1}{8}$ $\frac{1}{8}$

$\frac{1}{8}$ ◯ $\frac{1}{8}$

2.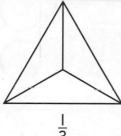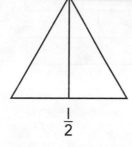

$\frac{1}{3}$ $\frac{1}{2}$

$\frac{1}{3}$ ◯ $\frac{1}{2}$

Spiral Review

3. Matt has 25 fish. Nine are angel fish, and the rest are guppies. How many fish are guppies?

_____ guppies

4. Divide the length model into fourths. Write the fraction for 2 parts.

$\dfrac{\square}{\square}$

Name _____

Fractions Equal to 1

Essential Question How do you know if a fraction is equal to 1 whole?

Learning Objective You will name and write fractions that describe a whole and are equal to 1.

Listen and Draw Real World

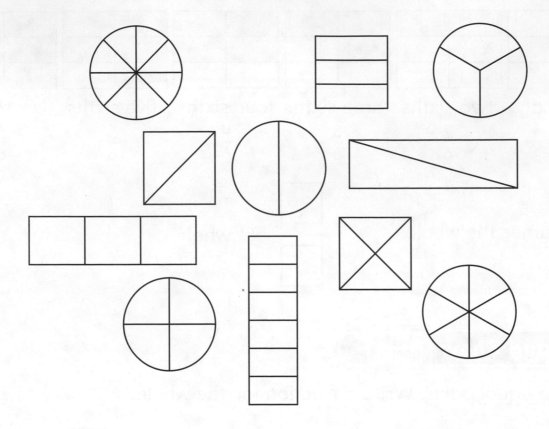

FOR THE TEACHER • Read the following problem. • Color all the models divided into halves blue. Color all the models divided into thirds green. Color all the models divided into sixths yellow.

Math Talk

Math Processes and Practices ❶

Look at the circle models. **Explain** how you know which part is the largest: one half, one third, or one sixth.

Model and Draw

This whole is divided into 6 equal parts. What fraction names this whole?

> The top number of the fraction tells how many of the equal parts are shaded and being counted.

Count all the sixths to make a whole.

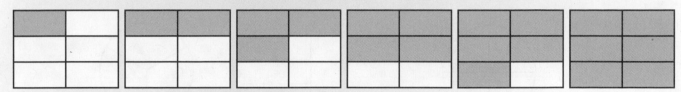

one sixth	two sixths	three sixths	four sixths	five sixths	six sixths
$\frac{1}{6}$	$\frac{2}{6}$	$\frac{3}{6}$	$\frac{4}{6}$	$\frac{5}{6}$	$\frac{6}{6}$

So, $\frac{6}{6}$ names the whole. $\dfrac{6}{6} = 1$ whole

Share and Show

Count the equal parts. Write a fraction for the whole.

1.  $\dfrac{3}{3} = 1$ whole

2. 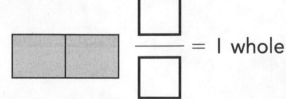 $\dfrac{}{} = 1$ whole

3. 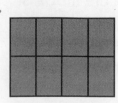 $\dfrac{}{} = 1$ whole

4. 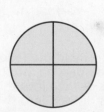 $\dfrac{}{} = 1$ whole

© Houghton Mifflin Harcourt Publishing Company

On Your Own

Count the equal parts. Write words to tell about the fraction. Write a fraction for the whole.

5.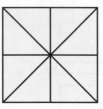

_____ fourths

6.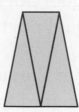

_____ thirds

7.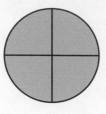

_____ eighths

8.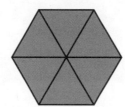

_____ sixths

9. **GO DEEPER** Lilly has two bagels that are the same size. She cuts both bagels into fourths. How many fourths does Lilly have from the two whole bagels?

_____ fourths

Problem Solving • Applications

10. Mr. Boyd works at a bakery. He baked three pies that are the same size. He cuts one pie into 2 equal parts. He cuts another pie into 4 equal parts and the last pie into 8 equal parts.

    Divide the first pie into 2 equal parts, the second pie into 4 equal parts, and the third pie into 8 equal parts. Write a fraction for each whole pie.

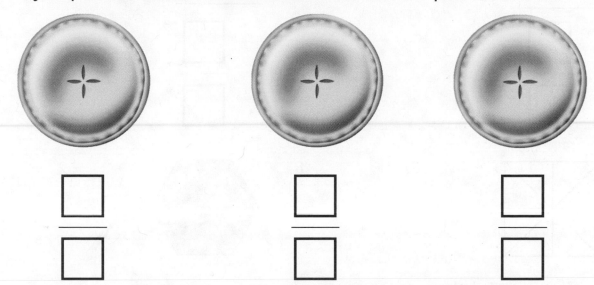

11. **THINK SMARTER** There are three pizzas that are the same size. A cheese pizza is cut into halves. A pepperoni pizza is cut into thirds. A veggie pizza is cut into sixths. Delaney chooses the pizza cut into the smallest slices. Which pizza does she choose? Draw to show your work.

    _____

 TAKE HOME ACTIVITY • Fold one sheet of paper into three equal parts and one sheet into four equal parts. Ask your child to name the fraction for each whole.

Name _____

Fractions Equal to 1
Count the equal parts.
Write a fraction for the whole.

Learning Objective You will name and write fractions that describe a whole and are equal to 1.

1.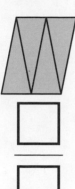

$$\frac{\square}{\square}$$

2.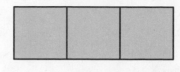

$$\frac{\square}{\square}$$

Problem Solving Real World

3. Cami has 2 watermelon slices that are the same size. She cut one slice into 3 equal parts. She cut the other slice into 8 equal parts. Write a fraction for each whole slice of watermelon.

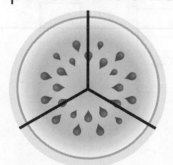 $\dfrac{\square}{\square}$  $\dfrac{\square}{\square}$

---

4. **WRITE** Math Are these two fractions equal? Explain.

_____

_____

Lesson Check

Count the equal parts. Write words to tell about the fraction. Write a fraction for the whole.

1.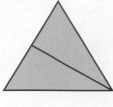

_____ halves

$\dfrac{\square}{\square}$

2.

_____ sixths

$\dfrac{\square}{\square}$

Spiral Review

3. Which unit fraction is less than $\frac{1}{6}$?

$\dfrac{1}{8}$ $\dfrac{1}{4}$ $\dfrac{1}{3}$ $\dfrac{1}{2}$

○   ○   ○   ○

4. Write the fraction for the shaded part.

    $\dfrac{\square}{\square}$

5. Divide the length model into fourths. Write the fraction for 3 parts.

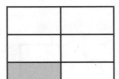

0   1 $\dfrac{\square}{\square}$

Name _____

Fractions of a Set

Essential Question How do you name and write fractions for equal parts of a set?

Learning Objective You will name and write fractions for equal parts of a set.

Listen and Draw

blue

□
―
□

orange

□
―
□

Math Talk

Math Processes and Practices ❶

Explain how the fraction for the blue cubes would change if all 6 cubes were blue.

FOR THE TEACHER • Read the following problem.
• Connect 2 blue cubes and 4 orange cubes. Draw the cube train on the workspace. Write a fraction for each cube color.

Model and Draw

Look at the number of equal parts.
What fraction of each set is red?

The top number tells how many equal parts are being counted. The bottom number tells how many equal parts are in the set.

 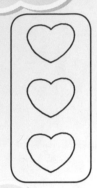

1 red part in the set
3 equal parts in the set

$\frac{1}{3}$ of the set is red.

1 red part in the set
2 equal parts in the set

$\frac{1}{2}$ of the set is red.

Share and Show MATH BOARD

Circle to show equal parts.
Color to show the fraction.

1. 2 equal parts

 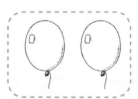

$\frac{1}{2}$

2. 4 equal parts

$\frac{1}{4}$

✓ 3. 3 equal parts

$\frac{1}{3}$

✓ 4. 6 equal parts

$\frac{1}{6}$

Name _____

Circle to show equal parts.
Color to show the fraction.

5. 3 equal parts

$\frac{1}{3}$

6. 8 equal parts

$\frac{1}{8}$

7. 2 equal parts

$\frac{1}{2}$

8. 4 equal parts

$\frac{1}{4}$

9. **GO DEEPER** There 3 equal parts of hearts.
What fraction of the set is red?
What fraction of the set is blue?

☐
―
☐ of the set is red.

☐
―
☐ of the set is blue.

Problem Solving • Applications

 WRITE Math

Count the equal parts.
Write the fraction of each set that is purple.

10.

$$\frac{\square}{\square}$$

11.

$$\frac{\square}{\square}$$

12. Use 4 counters to make a set to show the fraction.
Draw and color your set in the workspace.

$\frac{1}{2}$ of the set is yellow.

13. **THINK SMARTER** Miles has 4 green trains and
4 blue trains. What fraction of his trains
are blue?

_____ of the trains are blue.

 TAKE HOME ACTIVITY • Draw a set of 15 circles with your child.
Then ask him or her to color one third of the set.

Fractions of a Set

Circle to show equal parts.
Color to show the fraction

Learning Objective You will name and write fractions for equal parts of a set.

1.

$\frac{1}{4}$

2.

$\frac{1}{8}$

Count the equal parts.
Write the fraction for the set that is gray.

3.

Problem Solving

4. Some fish are in a tank. $\frac{1}{6}$ of the fish are orange.
   Draw a picture to show the fish in the tank.

5. **WRITE** Math Explain how you could draw a different
   set of fish in which $\frac{1}{6}$ of the fish are orange.

   _____

   _____

   _____

Lesson Check

Circle to show equal parts.
Color to show the fraction.

1.

$\dfrac{1}{3}$

Count the equal parts. Write the fraction for the set that is gray.

2.

□
—
□

Spiral Review

3. Write the fraction that names the shaded part.

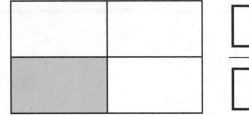

□
—
□

4. Which unit fraction is greater than $\dfrac{1}{3}$?

$\dfrac{1}{4}$ $\dfrac{1}{8}$ $\dfrac{1}{2}$ $\dfrac{1}{6}$

○   ○   ○   ○

5. Count the equal parts. Write words to tell about the fraction. Write a fraction for the whole.

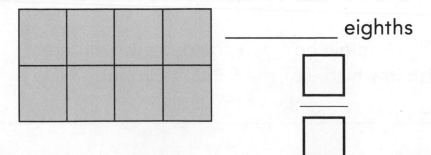

_____ eighths

□
—
□